WHO D

Also by Marvin Miller:

You Be The Jury
You Be The Jury 2
You Be The Jury 3
You Be The Detective
Your Own Super Magic Show
Your Own Christmas Magic Show

WHO DUNNIT?

How To Be a Detective
in Ten Easy Lessons.

Marvin Miller

Illustrated by Harry Venning

Scholastic Children's Books,
Scholastic Publications Ltd,
7-9 Pratt Street, London NW1 0AE

Scholastic Inc.,
730 Broadway, New York, NY 10003, USA

Scholastic Canada Ltd,
123 Newkirk Road, Richmond Hill,
Ontario, Canada L4C 3G5

Ashton Scholastic Pty Ltd,
PO Box 579, Gosford, New South Wales,
Australia

Ashton Scholastic Ltd,
Private Bag 1, Penrose, Auckland,
New Zealand

First published by Scholastic Inc. 1991
This edition published by Scholastic Publications Limited 1993

Text copyright © 1991 by Marvin Miller
Illustrations copyright © 1993 by Harry Venning

ISBN 0 590 55304 6

Typeset by A.J. Latham Ltd, Dunstable, Beds.
Printed by Cox and Wyman Ltd, Reading, Berks.

All rights reserved

10 9 8 7 6 5 4 3 2 1

for Wendy and Gary

Detective Casefiles

Introduction

This book will tell you all about being a master detective. The information is TOP SECRET. Share it only with a friend you can trust.

A detective needs sharp powers of observation. Evidence he or she discovers comes in many forms. The puzzles in this book will show you how to search for clues and how to understand what they mean.

Sometimes a detective needs to send a message to a partner. Just look inside to find out about secret codes and hiding places.

You also will discover important detective tips. But be careful when you use them. They are closely guarded secrets!

And finally, you will get a chance to do some mystery solving yourself. There are ten picture mystery stories in this book. You can follow along with Officer Fred Dumpty and put your detective skills into action. As you finish each casefile, turn to the Top Secret Solutions and see if your answers are on target.

I hope you have hours of fun with this book. So turn the page and get to work. You're on your way to becoming a master detective!

DETECTIVE CASEFILE 1

The Case of the
Soggy Suspect

Officer Fred Dumpty liked solving crimes almost as much as he liked eating. In fact, if he didn't spend so much time thinking about eating, he would surely have been promoted to the rank of detective by now.

One night, a hungry Officer Dumpty turned the corner onto Valley Street, looking for an open doughnut shop, when a sudden rainstorm began. As he rolled up the window of his police car, he saw a woman waving at him frantically.

His thoughts turning from food to crime, he raced to the scene and found Mrs Turner in tears.

"My handbag! A man just stole my handbag. He ran that way." Mrs Turner pointed to a small street up ahead.

"Did you get a good look at him?" Dumpty asked.

Mrs Turner held back sobs. "It happened so quickly. He came up from behind me and grabbed my handbag. When I turned around, all I could see was his back. I can't begin to describe him."

Dumpty put his foot down and sped through the rain in the direction Mrs Turner had pointed. It was a long street lined on both sides with small shops. Dumpty parked his police car and carefully checked the shops one by one. They were closed, and their doors were securely locked.

A restaurant at the end of the street was brightly lit. His stomach rumbling, Officer Dumpty went inside, where the smell of roast dinner wafting from the kitchen made his mouth water. But, keeping his mind on the business of detection, he walked over to a waitress who was cleaning a table.

"Did anyone come in here in the past ten minutes?" he asked.

"I don't know," she replied. "I've been in and out of the kitchen."

The restaurant was practically full. As Dumpty surveyed the room his eyes rested on two interesting things. One was a slice of delicious–looking apple pie under a glass lid. The other was a man sitting alone at a table.

When Officer Dumpty walked towards him, the man put down his coffee cup and looked up from a paperback book he was reading. Quite casually, Dumpty asked, "How long have you been here?"

"Almost an hour," the man answered. "I

heard you ask the waitress if she saw anyone come in. But I can't help you either, Officer. I've been reading this terrific mystery book. It's so frightening I can't put it down."

At that moment, Dumpty knew that he wouldn't have time for a bite to eat. Instead he said to the man, "I'd like you to come with me to police headquarters concerning a stolen handbag."

Examine the picture of Officer Dumpty talking to the man at the table. Why did Dumpty think he had caught the bag snatcher?

FILE ENTRY: Footprint Clues

Here are the normal footprints of a person walking. Notice the direction the feet point, the distances between steps, and the firm impressions of the heels and toes.

Now look at six sets of footprints that are a little more unusual. **Can you match each Set (1-6) with one of the descriptions (A-F)?**

Descriptions

A. Pulling a cart
B. Running
C. Very tall person walking
D. Pushing a wheelbarrow
E. Limping
F. Walking with a stick

1

2

3

4

5

6

FILE ENTRY: Ruler Code

A good way to send a secret message is with the help of a ruler. First draw a line at the left end of the ruler. Then print each letter of your secret message above the centimetre marks, like this:

S   E   N   D   H   E   L   P

```
|||||||||||||||||||||||||||||||||||||||||||||||||||||
  10  20  30  40  50  60  70  80
```

Finally, to disguise the message, add extra letters. Here's an example:

RST   ESLUIN   RADH   LHEBRUE   NLS   OPUR

```
|||||||||||||||||||||||||||||||||||||||||||||||||||||
  10  20  30  40  50  60  70  80
```

Now that you know the trick, **can you work out the secret message below?**

I   EWL SAY   IONATS AFL MON URU TMF   E

FILE ENTRY: Detective Tip

If you have a drawer where you keep secret things, here's a way to find out whether someone else has opened it.

With saliva, stick a hair across the crack in the drawer, as shown in the illustration:

If someone opens the drawer, the hair will become unstuck.

DETECTIVE CASEFILE 2

The Case of the Bald-Headed Suspect

"I came as fast as I could, Sergeant."
Officer Fred Dumpty stood panting in
the doorway to Sergeant Rider's office.

Dumpty had been called to the office in the
middle of a quick bite, and powdered sugar
from a doughnut coated the front of his
uniform.

"Close the door, Dumpty, and clean off your
uniform," said Rider gruffly, from behind his
desk. "I've told you to pay more attention to
your appearance."

Rider was furious, but Dumpty soon found
out that it wasn't only because of Dumpty's
uniform. In a low voice seething with anger,
Rider said, "We managed to capture Bart
Hargrove and we brought him here until
government officers arrive."

"That's great!" cried Dumpty. "He's wanted
in four counties. The chief superintendent will
give you a commendation."

"No, you idiot, he'll probably sack me.
Hargrove has just escaped. It'll cost me my job."

Though the sergeant often criticized Dumpty,

he wasn't a bad chap and he needed Dumpty's help. "Do we have any clues?" asked Dumpty.

"We have a report that a man fitting Hargrove's description stole a motor scooter and was heading east not more than twenty minutes ago."

"He can't get very far," said Dumpty. "If he's heading east, I can overtake him. But what does he look like?" Sergeant Rider handed him a wanted poster. "It's a shame this isn't a clear picture. But since Hargrove is as bald as a honeydew melon and is wearing prison clothes, he should be easy to recognize."

Rider groaned. "Not any more. He stole an officer's street clothes from his locker, then shoplifted another outfit from a clothes shop. We don't know what he's wearing now."

"Sounds bad, but I'm glad you have confidence in me to find him, Sarge."

"Don't call me Sarge," barked Rider, who did everything by the book. "And by the way, you're not finding anybody, I am — you're driving me."

In the police car, Dumpty told Rider that the motor scooter couldn't have travelled more than ten miles. "The furthest he could have got is Dover City." Minutes later, they arrived at the outskirts of town. As he passed Walden's Supermarket, Dumpty put on the brakes.

There was a motor scooter in the car park.

"Wait in the car while I check inside the shop," said Rider. "Maybe Hargrove stopped to buy food."

Sergeant, could you buy me a bag of crisps while you're in there? I haven't eaten lunch yet."

"Do you ever stop thinking about food, Dumpty? Buy it yourself."

Dumpty happily followed Rider into the shop. Inside, Rider spotted a suspicious-looking man at the checkout. He was wearing a big hat pulled down tight over his head. He seemed to fit the description of Hargrove. "Dumpty," whispered Rider triumphantly, from behind a display rack, "he must be Hargrove. He put on a hat to cover his bald head — why else would he be wearing a hat inside the shop? I'm going to arrest him." He started to pull out his revolver.

"Buutsaarg. . ."

"What did you say, Dumpty?"

Behind him, Dumpty swallowed the crisps he had been eating. (He was going to pay for them at the counter.) "But, Sarge, I think you're making a big mistake."

Rider's face turned red. "Who cares what you think? Look at you, crisps all over your uniform. A copper who doesn't pay attention to appearances isn't much of a copper."

Dumpty simply smiled and whispered something into Rider's ear. "As much as I hate to admit it, I suppose you're right, Dumpty. He's not our man. Let's continue into town before Bart Hargrove gets much further."

Examine the picture of Officer Dumpty and Sergeant Rider inside the supermarket. How did Dumpty know the man wasn't Bart Hargrove?

17

FILE ENTRY: Lip Reading

Some detectives read lips to learn valuable information. While on public surveillance a detective saw several suspicious-looking people enter a guarded door. Each was allowed inside by using a secret password that changed daily.

To the right is what the detective saw through her telescope during the six days of her surveillance. She took a picture of the person's lips just as the person was starting to pronounce the secret password.

Can you match the pictures (1-6) with the following passwords (A-F)?

A.
Eagle
B.
Microfilm
C.
Ooze

D.
Thread
E.
Apple
F.
Shadow

1

2

3

4

5

6

FILE ENTRY: Top Secret Tip

A small map (or a secret message) can be hidden inside a ball-point pen. Roll the map tightly around the ink tube and slip it back inside the outer shell.

FILE ENTRY: Mystery Riddle

Officers Davis and Horton were searching for a stolen box of rare coins that was hidden in a rubbish dump. They came to an abandoned sewer pipe, just large enough for one of them to squeeze through. Davis went through one end and Horton went through the other. Each crawled through the entire pipe and came out the other end. **How?**

DETECTIVE CASEFILE 3

The Case of the Snowball Slinger

Officer Dumpty stamped snow off his shoes as he opened the front door of Washington School. Mr Woodward had been the headmaster when Fred Dumpty attended Washington as a boy – and he was still the headmaster. Though grown-up, Dumpty was nervous at the thought of having to see Mr Woodward.

Inside, Mr Woodward frowned at Dumpty and said, "You're not very prompt, Fredrick." Dumpty winced. He hated being called Fredrick. "Sorry, Mr Woodward."

The headmaster pointed down the hall. "Vandalism, Dumpty! Someone threw a snowball through Mrs Gilbert's window."

The two men entered the classroom. Dumpty carefully examined the broken glass lying on the floor. Nearby, a puddle was all that was left of the snowball.

"What time did this happen, Mr Woodward?" asked Dumpty, somewhat shyly. It felt peculiar to be questioning his former headmaster.

"About an hour after school ended," Mr Woodward replied gruffly. "I'd suppose about half past four." Being interrogated by a former pupil was annoying.

"Have you got any idea who did it?"

"It must have been someone in Mrs Gilbert's class. It could have been Tommy Hummer. He's a trouble-maker. In fact, I punished him for throwing snowballs at some children during lunch break."

Officer Dumpty got Tommy's address from the school files and drove to the Hummers' house. He disliked solving cases at dinnertime. It was difficult for Dumpty to concentrate when he was hungry, which was often.

When he rang the bell, Mrs Hummer opened the door. Fred Dumpty introduced himself and stepped inside. He saw Tommy peering from behind his mother's back.

Dumpty described the act of vandalism to her and the fact that Tommy had been punished for throwing snowballs. Mrs Hummer smiled warmly and said, "He was probably just having some fun. Didn't you ever throw snowballs at kids when you were his age?"

Dumpty said yes, and at the same time became aware of the delightful smell of a roast cooking in the oven. Mrs Hummer noticed this and invited him to stay for dinner.

"Thanks for the offer, but now I have to ask a few more questions. Where was Tommy at half past four this afternoon?"

"He was here in this house, playing video games all afternoon," she replied, still smiling pleasantly.

"How can you be sure?"

"I get home from work at four o'clock every day. Today, Tommy was already home when I arrived. But enough questions, let's get ready for a delicious meal."

Dumpty glanced at Tommy, who had moved closer to his mother. "One last one. Did he leave the house at all?"

"No," said Mrs Hummer, the smile gone, her voice beginning to rise. "I told you he was here all afternoon! He came straight home after school."

"Well then," said Dumpty, "you'd both better come with me to the school. Tommy wasn't playing his video games all afternoon. He was outside when you came home."

Officer Dumpty continued. "You're covering up for him, so he must have been the one who threw the snowball. But I won't charge Tommy with mischief. It's up to the headmaster to decide on his punishment."

"You can forget about dinner, then," said Mrs Hummer in a huff.

Dumpty nodded sadly.

Examine the picture on the following page of Officer Dumpty speaking to Mrs Hummer. Why did he think she was lying??

FILE ENTRY: Detective Tip

If you want to walk up a flight of creaky stairs without making any noise, follow these directions. First take off your shoes. Then, walk on the outside tip of the steps. The stairs will squeak the least that way.

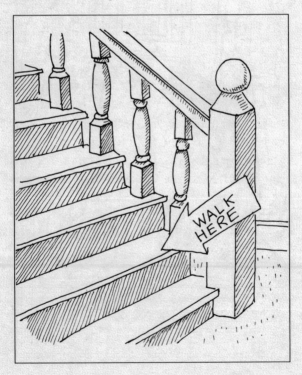

FILE ENTRY: Secret Graph Code

You can use ordinary graph paper to send a secret message to a friend. First, cut a strip from the graph paper and print all the letters of the alphabet in twenty six of the boxes. Your alphabet strip should look like this:

`A B C D E F G H I J K L M N O P Q R S T U V W X Y Z`

To create the secret message, lay the alphabet strip below the first row of boxes on a blank piece of graph paper. Draw a star or an X in the box the first letter in your message. Then slide the alphabet strip below the second row, and draw a star in the box above the second letter of your message.

Continue like this until your message is complete. For example, here is how to encode the message "BEWARE":

It may take too much graph paper to send a long message like this. But by using numbers instead of stars, you can re-use the same rows for different parts of your message. Instead of drawing a star in each box, write the number 1. When you get to the bottom of the piece of graph paper, go back to the top and continue your message, this time writing the number 2 in each box. If you get to the bottom again, continue at the top with the number 3, and so on. (Sometimes you may have to place more than one number in a box.)

If you like, you can also skip a row of boxes between words. That's been done in the following message. **Can you decipher what it says?**

FILE ENTRY: Mystery Riddle

When Henry joined the Glendale police force, his picture was on the front page of the town's weekly newspaper. Everyone thought he would help make the town safer. As time went by, Henry worked on many of Glendale's toughest cases, and was highly praised. But he never received a promotion. In fact, Henry was never even paid for his work on the police force? **Why?**

DETECTIVE CASEFILE 4

The Case of the Lost Locomotive

When Officer Fred Dumpty entered Bell's Hobby Shop, Mr Bell was leaning against the counter, head in hands, as if he were in pain.

Looking up, he said in a voice that cracked, "Nancy Gibson. She must have stolen the Silver Arrow. And to think I trusted her."

The Silver Arrow was the most expensive model locomotive in the shop — a collector's item that worked better than some real-life engines.

Mr Bell pointed to the display shelf, where a line of coaches sat on the tracks. The engine was missing.

Dumpty scratched his head and took out his notepad, musing to himself. How come the sergeant sends Mallory to investigate bank robberies, and I get stolen choo-choo trains? But then he thought: No case was too small for a great detective like Sherlock Holmes to solve, and no case is too small for Officer Dumpty! Speaking aloud, Dumpty said, "What makes you think it was the Gibson girl?"

The owner hesitated, as if he didn't really want to get Nancy in trouble. "Nancy loves collecting things — toy soldiers, thimbles, wind-up toys. And especially model trains. She always comes here after school and plays with the Silver Arrow. She wanted to buy it, but she said it would take a long time to save up for it with her pocket money."

"When do you think it was stolen?" Dumpty asked Mr Bell.

"It couldn't have been more than a half an hour ago," Mr Bell replied. "Around half past eight. I was closing my shop for the night and went into the back room. When I returned, the train was gone. That's when I phoned the police."

It was a long, hot drive to the Gibson house. Dumpty rolled down the window to cool off. To save petrol money, the sarge told his men to turn off their air-conditioning. Well, Sherlock Holmes didn't have air-conditioning at 221B Baker Street, either. When a sweaty Dumpty arrived, he rang the bell several times. No one answered. Dumpty decided to wait.

After fifteen minutes, Officer Dumpty knocked as loudly as he could. A minute or two later, Nancy Gibson opened the door.

"Where have you been?" Dumpty asked sharply. The heat was making him irritable.

"I was reading *Antique Model Railway* magazine in my shed in the back yard. I built the shed to keep all the things I collect. It's much cooler in there. With the door open, there's a nice breeze."

Officer Dumpty gave the girl his sternest look, one he had practised in front of the mirror. "Someone stole the Silver Arrow from Bell's. Do you know anything about it?"

Nancy Gibson stared at him, eyes wide with innocence. "Goodness me, Officer, it wasn't me. Take a look in my shed — I'll even let you in without a search warrant."

They walked to the back yard and opened the shed door. The room was pitch-black. Nancy lit the candle on the table.

"If you were reading in here," said Dumpty, "how come the candle is out?" Gotcha, thought the officer.

Nancy said coolly, "I blew it out when I went to see who was knocking."

Blast, thought Dumpty, she's quick. The officer scanned the room, filled with thimbles and toys and wind-up toys and model railway trains. But no Silver Arrow. Nancy shrugged her shoulders.

Sherlock would never have been outwitted by a thirteen-year-old, thought Dumpty, desperately. He looked at the room again and this time he had an idea. He turned to Nancy:

"Are you sure you were here tonight?"

She nodded with a smile.

"Well," said Dumpty, "I know for a fact you weren't in your shed when I rang your doorbell. At that moment, I suspect you were returning from Bell's Hobby Shop, and I'll bet you had the Silver Arrow with you. You must have used the back door so that I wouldn't see you arrive."

"How do you know that?" asked Nancy.

"Elementary," replied the officer.

Examine the picture of Officer Dumpty speaking to Nancy Gibson. Why did he think she was lying?

FILE ENTRY: Spotting Spots

Detectives can discover clues by studying spots. Here are different marks left by a person eating a chocolate ice-cream cone. The marks were made by the dripping ice cream.

Can you match the drops (1-6) with the descriptions of the person eating the cone (A-F)?

A. Standing on the ground

B. Sitting on top of a ladder

C. Standing in the same place for several minutes

D. Walking towards your right

E. Walking towards your left

F. Standing on a balcony above a wall

1

2

3

4

5

6

FILE ENTRY: Top Secret Tip

Using a water glass, you can overhear a subject's conversation in the next room. Hold the glass tightly against the wall and put your ear to its open end. The larger the glass and the thinner its sides, the better you will be able to hear.

FILE ENTRY: Mystery Riddle

Two police officers hid behind a hedge to watch for speeders they could give tickets to. One officer looked up the road and the other looked down it, so as to cover both directions.

"Ann," said one, without turning his head, "what are you smiling at?"

How could he tell that Ann was smiling?

DETECTIVE CASEFILE 5

The Case of the Darling Dog

Officer Fred Dumpty was barely awake. It was the start of his morning rounds, and he lazily cruised down Greenleaf Street, on the outskirts of town, enjoying the peace and quiet.

"Help! Police! Murder!" he heard suddenly.

Dumpty nearly jumped out of his seat. Across the street, a woman holding a little dog was screaming hysterically. Dumpty pulled his car over to find out what had happened.

"My little Terrie has been brutally attacked by Billy Harris," wailed Mrs Smithers. "I demand you arrest that hooligan and throw him in jail."

"Is Terrie your daughter?" asked Dumpty urgently. "Shall I call an ambulance?"

"No, you fool, Terrie is my sweet darling dog. Can't you see the awful lump on the head she got from that stone?"

Indeed, there was a small lump on the top of the dog's head. Slightly annoyed by Mrs Smithers's tone of voice, Dumpty said, "She'll be fine. Now tell me what happened."

"It's that newspaper boy, Billy Harris," said Mrs Smithers, placing Terrie on the ground. Instantly, the dog started growling at Dumpty.

"Why don't you start at the beginning," said Dumpty, nervously watching the dog.

"It was eight o'clock this morning and I had just let Terrie outside. A few minutes later I heard something hit my front door. And then my Terrie let out a big howl."

Dumpty walked over to the door to look at the two large stones in front of it, one of which had hit Terrie. As he did so, Terrie raced up and clamped her jaws on Dumpty's leg. Dumpty tried to shake her off.

"Police brutality!" yelled Mrs Smithers.

"Get her off me or I'll give her a lift to the dog pound."

After Mrs Smithers retrieved her dog, Dumpty tried to calm her down.

"How do you know it was Billy Harris?"

"When I ran outside, I saw the back of Billy's bike in the distance. He had just delivered my newspaper and was on his way to the next house down the road. Billy never did like Terrie. The other day I saw him kick her away from his bike. Terrie was just being friendly, weren't you, my darling lambkins?"

"I bet," muttered Dumpty under his breath.

He didn't want Mrs Smithers to file a complaint with his sergeant.

Officer Dumpty examined the fresh bike track in the lane in front of the Smithers's house. "I'll bring Billy back to the scene of the the crime," he said.

A short time later, Billy pedalled up to the Smithers's house, Dumpty driving behind him. Terrie started growling at Billy, and Mrs Smithers warned, "Keep away from my dog, you beast!"

Dumpty was reluctant to get out of his car while Terrie was off the lead, but a policeman must be brave. He stepped up to Billy and gazed sternly at the boy. "Did you throw stones at Mrs Smithers's dog while delivering her paper?"

Billy looked scared. "No way," he said. "I like dogs."

Dumpty turned to Mrs Smithers. "You didn't see Billy throw the stones. Could it have been anyone else?"

"Well. . ." said the woman slowly. "No other bicycles have gone by, I'm sure. But I heard some noises outside just before the stone hit my front door. It sounded like kids laughing. It might have been one of them."

"It probably was," said Dumpty, who had been thinking furiously. He wanted to solve

the case and get away from that vicious dog as
quickly as possible. "Billy Harris never threw
stones at your dog."

**Examine the picture on the following page of
Officer Dumpty speaking with Mrs Smithers.
How did he know it wasn't Billy who threw
the stones?**

FILE ENTRY: Voice Disguise

A detective some-times needs to disguise his or her voice when speaking on the telephone. A good way to do this is to talk with a pencil between your teeth. (It takes practice to do it well!)

FILE ENTRY: Telephone Code

The numbers on your telephone can be used to send a secret code. Except for 1 and 0, there are three letters above each number. For example, 8 goes with the letters T, U and V.

To write a note in telephone code, find each letter in your secret message on the phone diagram. Then write down the number instead. Put a small line above the number to show whether it is the first, middle, or last letter of the number. For example:

\
T would be written as **8**

|
U would be written as **8**

/
V would be written as **8**

Since there is no Q or Z on the phone, let the number 1 represent Q and the number 0 represent Z.

Here is how to decode the word DANGER

\\ | \ | |
326437

Can you work out this
secret message?

/|\/ \/\/ \| \\|// ///// \/|| /| |/||/|
5387 7529 26 27745 36657 5653 66 266643

FILE ENTRY: Making a Compass

If you are on a secret mission and get lost, you can make a compass by using your watch.

Hold the watch flat and point the hour hand in the direction of the sun.

Then draw an imaginary line from the centre of the watch mid-way between the number 12 and the hour hand. The line will point almost directly south.

Here is an example:

FILE ENTRY: Mystery Riddle

Ronald was running towards home. Suddenly, he saw a masked man. He quickly stopped, turned round, and began running back in the direction he had come from. Almost at once, though, he deliberately slid to the ground and stopped. **Why?**

DETECTIVE CASEFILE 6

The Case of the
Unfortunate Fan

After signing off on his car radio, a famished Officer Fred Dumpty took one last bite of his sugar-glazed doughnut, turned on the siren (next to eating, he liked doing this best), and raced to Hargrove Auditorium. Jimmy Hansen was nervously pacing outside.

"You got here just in time," said Jimmy. "He's still hiding in the car park."

The boy got into the car and Dumpty began cruising past rows of parked cars. . . until it dawned on him that he didn't know who he was looking for — or why. It was a bad way to begin a case. "What happened, Jimmy?"

"Someone stole my wallet out of my back pocket while I was waiting to get into the concert. Gastric Juice is the most radical heavy metal band around, and now I'll never get to see them play." From what Dumpty had heard of this group, he thought Jimmy should feel fortunate. Gastric Juice couldn't compare with the rock 'n' roll he had enjoyed as a youngster.

Jimmy fought back tears. Dumpty tried to console him by mentioning how he had once missed the chance to see a Beatles concert. "Who are the Beatles?" asked Jimmy, wiping his eyes on his sleeve.

"Never mind," said Dumpty, suddenly feeling old. "Tell me your story."

"I was in the middle of the crowd, waiting for the main doors to open. Suddenly I felt something pulling at my back pocket. When I reached for my wallet, it was gone. Then I saw this chap behind me push his way out of the crowd. He was the one who took my wallet. It had twenty-five pounds in it and my concert ticket."

"Did you get a good look at him?" asked Dumpty.

"No, he was running towards the car park when I spotted him. He was wearing a red jacket and a baseball cap. I ran after the man, but lost him. He must have ducked behind some cars."

Looking sadly out of the police car window, Jimmy said, "I bought the ticket a month ago. Now I'm missing everything."

After an hour driving round, Dumpty drove to the car park exit and turned off the motor. "There are so many places to hide, we'll never find him. Let's wait here. This is the only way out, and he'll have to pass us. In the meantime, do you think you can run over to the food stall and buy me a couple of hot dogs?"

When the concert ended, the front doors of the auditorium opened and people began pushing their way out, streaming past them. While Officer Dumpty was finishing off his frankfurter, Jimmy grabbed his arm.

"Over there. There's someone wearing a red jacket and baseball cap."

Dumpty dabbed the mustard off his mouth, walked over to the man, and asked him his name. The man's hat was shoved down over his forehead. A pair of eyes squinted at Dumpty. "Brad Lathrop," he said. "What's the problem, Officer?"

"I'm looking for someone who stole a wallet. He's been hiding in the car park."

"Well, it wasn't me," said Lathrop. "I was watching the concert from a front row seat."

"Can you prove it?" asked Dumpty. "Did anyone you know see you there?"

"No, I was sitting next to strangers. But here is my ticket. It proves I was at the concert."

The man dug into his pocket and, with a smirk, handed a ticket to Officer Dumpty. The ticket was for the Gastric Juice concert, all right.

Dumpty turned to Jimmy. "Could this be yours?"

Jimmy shook his head. "I can't be sure. There were no seat numbers, just a ticket number. And I can't remember what my ticket number was."

The man in the red jacket look relieved. "I told you that's my ticket," he said. "What a concert! Gastric Juice sang all their big hits, like 'Everything Is Rotten.'" As Lathrop started to sing the song, Dumpty tuned him out and began thinking. Then he spoke.

"I think you're lying. You never bought a ticket to the concert. You came here just to rob someone. I'm taking you to police headquarters."

"Hey," shouted the man, "you've got nothing on me."

But Dumpty did.

Examine the picture on the following page of Dumpty speaking to the man in the red jacket. How did he know he had caught the pickpocket?

FILE ENTRY: Secret Line Messages

The drawing below has all the lines needed to make every letter of the alphabet. It can be used to send secret messages.

For example, if the first letter of your message is an N, the code would be 4132. To unscramble the code, place a piece of paper over the above diagram and draw a line from 4 to 1, from 1 to 3, and from 3 to 2. Your N will look like this:

For some letters, you need to lift your pencil. Use a comma to indicate a new line. For example, the letter K is 68, 293.

Letters can be written more than one way. For example, the letter H could be written as 14, 57, 23; or 41, 95, 86 (as well as several other ways).

Can you work out the word below?

215734 1432 862793
41695 862793 68
437512 2157, 543

FILE ENTRY: Handwriting Analysis

Sometimes a detective can tell something about a person by studying his or her handwriting. Below are six messages.

Can you match each message (1-6) with the description (A-F) of the person who wrote it?

A. Was written by an Englishman
B. Was traced from someone else's note
C. Contains a hidden message

D. Was written by someone disguising his or her handwriting
E. Was written by a left-handed person
F. Was written in a hurry

16/7/93

Follow my directions to find the hidden money First go to the rock ~~&~~ by the oak tree. It is twelve paces to the rock

1

16/7/93

Follow my dIrections to fiNd The Hidden monEy. First go To the Rock by thE oak tree. It is twelve paces to thE rock.

2

7/16/93

Follow my directions to find the hidden money. First go to the rock by the oak tree. It is twelve paces to the rock.

3

16/7/93

Follow my directions to find the hidden money. First go to the rock by the oak tree. It is twelve paces to the rock.

4

16/7/93

Follow my directions to find the hidden money. First go to the rock by the oak tree. It is twelve paces to the rock.

5

16/7/93

Follow my directions to find the hidden money. First go to the rock by the oak tree. It is twelve paces to the rock.

6

FILE ENTRY: Mystery Riddle

Frank Cummings worked for the Sunshine Bus Company for fourteen years. He was one of their most reliable drivers. One day a policeman saw Frank going the wrong way down a one-way street. But the officer didn't give Cummings a ticket. **Why?**

DETECTIVE CASEFILE 7

The Case of the Bumbling Burglar

Sundays were usually slow at police head-quarters. Officer Fred Dumpty was at his desk munching a doughnut and puzzling over the Sunday crossword. He was just about to fill in the answer to 6 Down ("Italian pie" – PIZZA, one of his favourite foods), when the phone rang. "Great," Dumpty grumbled "Just when I was about to write my first answer in one of these things."

"Hello, police? This is Greg Winters," whispered a voice. "Quick, send someone to 28 Skyline Drive. There's someone in my bedroom, I can hear. . ."

The voice faded away. Dumpty could hear a sharp crack as the phone receiver hit something – probably the floor. Then he heard the muted voice of Mr Winters shouting, "Hey, drop that! The police are on the way, they'll find you!"

Dumpty scrambled to his patrol car. Yes, he thought as he drove towards Skyline Drive, the police are on their way. He enjoyed being a figure of law and order, and prided himself on his perfect crime-solving record.

When Dumpty arrived at the Winters' house, the front door was locked. At the rear of the house he found a concrete patio, and behind it a large wooded area. The back door was open. Preparing himself for the worst, Dumpty pulled out his revolver.

"I'm over here," shouted a voice behind him. Dumpty swung round and saw a man stumbling out of the woods. He was wearing a bathrobe and slippers. The slippers were covered with bits of wood and brambles.

"I'm Greg Winters," the man panted. "I'm afraid I lost him. He ran off towards the main road."

"Tell me what happened here," said Dumpty.

"I was reading in my study," said Winters, "when I heard funny noises. At first I thought it was children playing in the street, but then I heard drawers opening and closing in my bedroom." Winters gestured towards the other end of the house. "That's when I called the police. Was it you I spoke to?"

Officer Dumpty nodded and glanced at the man's feet. Winters's slippers had rabbit faces on them. "What were you doing in the woods?" he asked.

"When I was on the phone to you," Winters explained, "I saw a man run into the woods. I dropped the phone and ran after him. I can usually run pretty quickly, but these slippers held me back."

"Can you describe the man?" asked Dumpty.

"Well, he was wearing jeans and a grey sweatshirt, and he had brown hair. But I only saw him from the back. I'm afraid it's not much help."

Dumpty looked at Greg's worried face. "We'd better go inside and see if anything is missing."

"I heard the man go into my cupboard," said Greg. "I keep my coin collection in there. I hope he didn't steal it. It's worth a lot of money." He added, "At least I'm insured."

Dumpty took off his hat and scratched his head. He wanted to wrap up the case quickly, because he was getting hungry again. "You know, Mr Winters, I'll bet your coin collection *is* missing. But it wasn't stolen. I think you made up this story so that you could collect the insurance money."

Examine the picture of Officer Dumpty talking to Greg Winters. Why did Dumpty suspect that the robbery was a fraud?

FILE ENTRY: Questioning the Suspect

Asking the right questions can help a detective solve a crime or catch a criminal. Here are three suspects. After reading the facts, what *one* question would tell you whether or not the suspect was guility?

SUSPECT 1

You board a train in search of a criminal, whom you suspect is on the train and heading for Greenville, fifty miles away. You believe he plans to flee the country from the Greenville airport. A man who looks like your suspect is reading a newspaper in the last carriage. The conductor tells you the man has no identification but claims to be going to Greenville for some shopping and plans to return that evening. **What do you ask the suspect?**

FILE ENTRY: Questioning the Suspect

SUSPECT 2

You trail a spy to a small farm village. You suspect he arrived that morning and is disguised as a farmer. You see a man who is hoeing a field and is dressed like a farmer. His dungarees are dirty. Beads of perspiration dot his forehead. He seems nervous as you approach him. **What do you ask him?**

FILE ENTRY: Questioning the Suspect

SUSPECT 3

You arrive at a mansion where there has been a burglary. The owner claims he found a window open and a valuable antique statue missing from the hall. His dog, Brutus, sniffs the carpet where the statue once stood. The owner suspects his servant committed the robbery, but the burglar could have been a stranger. **What do you ask the owner?**

FILE ENTRY: Under Surveillance

Sometimes a detective must watch a suspect without the person knowing he or she is being observed. You can pretend to be reading a magazine while still keeping your suspect under surveillance. Here's how:

Cut out a small circle from the front pages of an open magazine. Then, tape a small mirror on the opposite page.

Pretend to be reading the magazine. If your suspect is in front of you, watch him or her through the peephole. If he or she is behind you, hold the magazine so you can see him or her in the mirror.

FILE ENTRY: Mystery Riddle

Officer Franklin responded to a police call. A woman was sitting on a tenth-floor window sill and threatening to jump. There were no awnings or ledges to break her fall to the concrete pavement below. As Franklin got out of his police car, she suddenly fell off the sill. But she wasn't hurt. **What happened?**

DETECTIVE CASEFILE 8

The Case of the
Down-and-Out
Delivery Man

Officer Fred Dumpty was taking a beating. The man he was fighting swung his fist and hit Dumpty square in the nose. Dumpty was knocked for six.

"Are you all right?" asked his opponent, trainee copper Steve Porter.

The two men were boxing in the makeshift ring in the basement of police headquarters; the policemen used it to keep fit. Dumpty staggered to his feet and sat up against the ropes. "I guess I'm no Mike Tyson," he laughed, removing his boxing gloves.

You're not even a Pee-wee Herman," replied Porter. Dumpty was too mad to answer the cocky young copper.

The next day, because he was so bruised, Dumpty was given duty at the front desk of the police station. Nothing much happened until that afternoon, when a young man lurched through the front door.

Dumpty recognized him. It was Dennis Bean, the delivery man who worked at Walter's Chemist.

Dennis looked faint; his face was bruised and his lip was slightly swollen. Dumpty helped him to a chair and handed him an ice bag. "Tell me what happened," said Dumpty.

"Around two o'clock every afternoon, Mr Walter gets me to take the money from the cash register over to Middle Land Bank. Today, while I was driving down Market Street, I saw a man on a motorbike parked by the side of the road. He flagged me down.

"I stopped my van to help him. The money was in a bag on the front seat next to me. When I opened the door and got out, he rushed over, grabbed my shoulder with one hand, and pinned me against the side of my van."

Dennis took out a handkerchief and blew his nose hard.

"Then he punched me in the face. I slid down to the ground. I must have blacked out for a minute. When I woke up, the money was gone."

Just at that moment, Officer Steve Porter walked past the two men. "Hey," he said to Dennis, chuckling, "I know Dumpty didn't hit you. His punch wouldn't hurt a flea."

Ignoring Porter, Dumpty grabbed a pencil and a police form. The sudden movement made his badly bruised nose throb. "I'll need a description for our patrol cars. What did he look like?"

Dennis thought for a minute. "He had on a motorcycle helmet so I couldn't make out his face. But he was tall. Maybe six feet or more, and really strong. Like this chap here." He pointed at Porter.

"Anything else?" asked Dumpty.

Dennis shook his head. "I can't remember. It all happened so quickly. But I do remember the muscles bulging out of his black T-shirt."

Dumpty looked at Dennis Bean's battered face. "So he knocked you out with just one punch?"

"He must have been a professional fighter or something," said Dennis. "He just wound up and hit me. One punch and I was out like a light."

Officer Porter, who was still listening, said, "This motorbike chap sounds like he might give me a good fight — or at least a better one than Fred gave me yesterday."

Battling the urge to hurl it at Porter, Officer Dumpty put down his pencil. His throbbing nose made concentrating difficult — but it helped him sort out the problem. He gave a disdainful glance at Porter, then stared hard at Dennis Bean.

"Where did you hide the money?"

Dennis straightened up and grabbed the sides of his chair. "What do you mean?"

"There was no man on a motorcycle," said Dumpty. "Why don't you tell me what really happened before you get into deeper trouble?"

Officer Porter looked at Dumpty with his mouth open in astonishment.

Examine the picture of Officer Dumpty questioning Dennis Bean. How did he know the delivery man had lied about the robbery?

FILE ENTRY: Shopping List Code

A good way to hide a secret message is to make it look like a shopping list.

The number in front of each item tells your friend, who will read the message, the number of letters to count. For example, the letter A could be coded as "5 pizzas," since A is the fifth letter in the word PIZZAS. If there is no number next to an item, the first letter of the word should be used.

The shopping list below encodes the message HOORAY:

Now can you find
the secret message
in this shopping list?

SOUR CREAM
5 APPLES
2 DETERGENT
3 MAYONNAISE
2 CORN OIL
2 BUTTER
  TOOTHPASTE
2 SOAP
6 RAISINS
2 MILK
  GRAPES
  HAM
  TISSUES

FILE ENTRY: Popcorn Tip

Do you have brothers or sisters who like to sneak into your room at night to borrow things? Here's a way to make a burglar alarm so that you can catch them.

First, you need a small, narrow box that is open at the top. You can make one by using the cover of a matchbox, and by sealing one end of it with tape to make a bottom.

Fill the box with unpopped popcorn or uncooked rice. Then cut a piece of thread about six inches long, and tape one end of the thread to the box. Finally, place the box on top of the frame of the door to your room, and tape the other end of the thread to the top of the door.

If the door is opened, the box will fall and its contents will spill out, waking you up.

FILE ENTRY: Mystery Riddle

A policeman arrested two girls for spraying paint on a stop sign. The girls looked exactly alike. They were born on the same day in the same year and they had the same parents. But the girls were not twins. **How could this be?**

DETECTIVE CASEFILE 9

The Case of the Diner Disasters

Cruising through town early one morning, Officer Fred Dumpty felt grumpy. He was on a diet. For breakfast, Dumpty usually ate bacon and pancakes with plenty of syrup, a glass of milk, sausages, buttered toast, some orange juice, and a muffin. All he had had today was cereal with skimmed milk. "I ate fifteen minutes ago and already I'm hungry. I'm never going to last until lunchtime." Though he didn't do it on purpose, Dumpty soon found himself driving down Maple Street, towards an area of town that had a lot of restaurants. None of the restaurants were open yet, and the pavements were empty.

As he passed Pulski's Restaurant, Dumpty noticed something strange and stopped the car. Outside the locked front door of Pulski's, was the morning's bakery delivery stacked up. Dumpty observed that several pies and cakes had been removed from their boxes, and that someone had taken big bites out of them. A large brown paper bag full of dinner rolls had been ripped apart and scattered across the pavement. On the pavement was a squashed lemon meringue pie. Imagine ruining all this good food, Dumpty thought sadly. He grabbed his radio mike. "There's been some vandalism and theft at Pulski's. Better tell Mr Pulski to come over quickly."

About ten minutes later, the shop owner arrived. "What a catastrophe!" he shouted. "Whoever did this should go to jail."

"Calm down, Mr Pulski," said Dumpty. "I'm on the job, so you can be confident the case will be solved."

That statement did not seem to put Mr Pulski's mind at ease. "This is the third incident this week," said the unhappy owner. "Monday someone squirted tomato sauce across the front window. Tuesday we kept getting takeaway orders over the phone for addresses that didn't exist. And now today, this."

Dumpty bent down and examined the squashed lemon meringue pie. A bicycle had ridden over it. One of its tyres had left a short trail.

"I'll bet it's those Thomas kids," muttered Mr Pulski. "I chased them away from the front of my restaurant a few days ago, but they kept riding past with their bikes and making a noise, and they almost knocked down one of my customers." Mr Pulski pointed in the direction of the tyre track: "See. They live in that direction, a few miles down. Hey Dumpty, you can get your nose out of the pie now and check up on the kids. Come on, Dumpty, I'll give you a piece of cake if you're that hungry."

"No thanks," sighed the policeman, getting up, "I'm on a diet."

It wasn't long before Dumpty pulled up to the Thomas' house. As he got out of the car, he heard noises coming from the open garage. There were Tim and Kim huddled over a bicycle.

"Where have you kids been for the last hour?" asked Dumpty. Tim nudged his sister with his elbow. Kim straightened up. "We've been cleaning my bike."

"Yeah," said Tim, "we've been cleaning her bike. Is that against the law?"

"Someone broke into bags of food in front of a restaurant in Maple Street," said Dumpty sternly. "Let me have a look at those tyres."

"It wasn't us," said Tim. "We haven't been near Pulski's since Monday."

Dumpty examined the front and back whitewall tyres. The rear tyre looked as if it had just been washed. It was still wet.

"How come you kids only cleaned just one of the tyres?"

"Uhh, we were just about to do the front," said Tim.

"Uhh, we ran out of soap," said Kim at the same instant.

"Well, I think both of you are lying," said Dumpty. "You were the ones who vandalised Pulski's Restaurant. And you cleaned the rear tyre because it was covered with lemon meringue."

Examine the picture on the following page of Officer Dumpty in front of Pulski's Restaurant. How did he know the Thomas kids were lying?

FILE ENTRY: Clue Search

When a detective searches for tiny clues (or when he or she searches for a lost object), it is important to see that none of the areas is skipped over. Here's how to do a really thorough search.

Inside a house or building, divide the rooms into areas. Then slowly examine each.

Outside a house, divide the area into a grid (stretch string or use wooden stakes). Then move through the grid as shown by the dotted line.

To search a very large area, use an ever-widening circle. Start at the centre and work outwards in a spiral.

FILE ENTRY: Pigpen Code

These diagrams are the key to a secret alphabet code you can use to send a hidden message. It's called a "pig-pen code" because each letter is in a compartment, or pen, that has a unique shape.

To send your message, draw the outline of the compartment each letter is in, including a dot if there is one. For example, here is how to send the message "WATCH OUT":

Can you decipher this secret message?

FILE ENTRY: Mystery Riddle

Officer Neale chased a robber who was escaping in a getaway car. The policeman managed to overtake him, even though his squad car had a flat tyre. **How could this be?**

DETECTIVE CASEFILE 10

The Case of the Stolen Exam

Officer Fred Dumpty was going through some very old maths tests he had taken as a student. "I don't know why I kept these," he said to himself. "Mr Erwin always took off points because of food stains and crumbs on the paper. But who could get through an hour-long exam without *some* refreshment?"

Just then the phone rang. "Hello, Fredrick? This is Erwin at the Washington School." What a coincidence, thought Dumpty. "I hate to bother you but I have a problem and need your help."

"Of course, Mr Erwin. What is it?" Dumpty asked.

"Someone got into my desk, Fredrick, and stole the answers to the final exam. It's just happened — I was only out of my office a couple of minutes. I need to find the thief quickly or I'll have to write a new exam for the children to take during their holiday. You remember how boring summer school is, don't you, Fredrick?"

Dumpty checked his watch. It was half past

four. "Are any children still in the school?" he asked.

"Only Ms Fernandez's students. They're having a dress rehearsal for a play."

"Okay. Keep everyone there. I'll be over straight away. And please don't call me Fredrick."

Within ten minutes, Officer Dumpty was knocking on Mr Erwin's office door. He fought back the painful memories of maths lessons.

"Hello, Fredrick!" (He pronounced it "Fred-er-rick.") "Glad you're here. Now, the answers were in the top drawer of my desk, here."

Dumpty examined the room. Noticing a glass on one of the filing cabinets, he asked, "Is this your glass of orange juice, Mr Erwin?"

The teacher's face brightened. "No, it must have been left by the person who stole the answers."

With his fingertips, Dumpty picked up the glass by its edge and held it up to the light, studying it carefully.

"This glass has no fingerprints," said Dumpty. He paused to think for a moment. "Does anyone in the play have a costume with gloves?"

"Good thinking, Fredrick! I'll run over to the auditorium and check."

A few minutes later, Mr Erwin returned with two children, one dressed as a dog, the other as a queen.

"Take off your masks," said Dumpty, "and tell me your names."

The queen lifted her bulky crown off her head and said, "Thank you, we've been wearing these things all afternoon. My name is Kelly."

The dog had been struggling to get his mask off and finally did so with Mr Erwin's help. "I'm Tony," he said. "Why did you bring us here?"

"Well," Dumpty explained, "some exam papers were stolen from Mr Erwin's desk. We found a glass here with no fingerprints on it, so we worked out that the thief might have had gloves on. Tony, is this your glass?"

"No, sir. See, I've got my own glass," Tony held up a glass of juice.

"But why is your glass almost full?" asked Dumpty. "Kelly said you have been rehearsing for a while."

"I, um, I've finished one glass already. This is my second. I was just drinking it when Mr Erwin fetched me from the auditorium."

Dumpty turned to Kelly. "Then is this *your* glass, Kelly?"

"No, it's not. This is the only glass I've had." She held up an almost empty glass of juice.

Dumpty nodded and solemnly walked over to Tony.

"Why don't you give the answer sheets back to your teacher, Tony. You're in enough trouble already."

Examine the picture of Dumpty with Tony and Kelly. How did he know the boy had taken the answers?

FILE ENTRY: Police Lineup

It was almost midnight when Frank O'Neill flagged down a police car on the main road. He could barely speak as he told the policeman that he had been attacked on a country road about a half mile away. His watch and wallet had been stolen. It was dark and he could not see his attacker.

O'Neill said that when he tried to get away, the robber grabbed his shoulder with one hand and punched him in the face with the other. From his picture over the page, you can see the injury was not very serious.

A police search located five persons in the area who were unable to produce an alibi for the time of the attack. They are pictured in the police line-up over the page.

Can you pick out the robber?

FILE ENTRY: Pack-of-Cards Code

You can send a secret message to a friend using an old pack of cards. The cards should have pictures on the backs. Arrange the cards so all the pictures are turned in the same direction.

Separate the cards into suits. Then, for each suit, put the cards in order from ace to king. Now, stack the cards with the ace of spades on the top, followed by all the hearts, all the diamonds, and all the clubs.

You are ready to write your secret message. Square the pack neatly and hold the cards tightly together. With a pencil, print your secret message around the sides of the pack.

To hide your message, all you have to do is mix up the cards. Turn the top half of the pack round so the pictures on the backs face in the opposite direction. Then shuffle the two halves together and your message will completely vanish.

When your friend gets the pack, he or she arranges the backs so they all face one way. Then he or she places the cards in the order you originally had them.

Your secret message will reappear around the edges!

FILE ENTRY: Mystery Riddle

When Officer Wallace patrolled his beat, it took him one hour and twenty minutes to walk one way. Without walking any faster, it took him only eighty minutes to return. **How come?**

TOP SECRET SOLUTIONS

DETECTIVE CASEFILE 1
THE CASE OF THE
SOGGY SUSPECT

The picture shows that the man's jacket is dripping wet. This means he must have been outside during the rainstorm. Since it began raining just as Mrs Turner's handbag was stolen, the man could not have been in the restaurant for an hour, as he said he was.

Footprint Clues
1. B (running)
2. E (limping)
3. D (pushing a wheelbarrow)
4. A (pulling a cart)
5. C (very tall person walking; notice the long strides, which would be made by someone with long legs)
6. F (walking with a stick)

Ruler Code
Wait for me.

DETECTIVE CASEFILE 2
THE CASE OF THE
BALD-HEADED SUSPECT

Dumpty suddenly remembered that one of the items the shopper bought was a comb. The stranger couldn't have been the escaped criminal. Bart Hargrove was completely bald, and would have no reason to buy a comb. It seems that Dumpty did pay attention to appearances after all.

Lip Reading
1. E
2. A
3. F
4. D
5. B
6. C

Mystery Riddle
They crawled through the sewer pipe at different times.

DETECTIVE CASEFILE 3
THE CASE OF THE
SNOWBALL SLINGER

If Mrs Hummer arrived home after Tommy, her coat would be hanging on top of his. But the picture shows that Tommy's coat is on top of his mother's. Therefore, he must have arrived home later in the afternoon than his mother.

Secret Graph Code
Meet me in the park after school.

Mystery Riddle
Henry was a police dog.

DETECTIVE CASEFILE 4
THE CASE OF THE
LOST LOCOMOTIVE

Nancy Gibson said she was looking through a magazine with the shed door open. But the melted wax was on the front of the candle. If Nancy had been reading by candlelight, the breeze would have caused the dripped wax to spill down the other side of the candle — away from the door. Sherlock Holmes would have been proud of Dumpty.

Spotting Spots
A. 2
B. 6 (From higher up, the drop makes a harder splash)
C. 3
D. 4
E. 1
F. 5 (This spot is running down the wall, while all the others are on the floor.)

Mystery Riddle
The police officers were facing each other.

DETECTIVE CASEFILE 5
THE CASE OF THE
DARLING DOG

If Billy had thrown both the newspaper and the stones from his bicycle, he would have had to slow down to do it. Then the tyre from his bike would have made a wobbly line as he tried to keep his balance, like the line leading up to his bike in the picture. But the track that Billy's bike made earlier, when he delivered the paper, is straight.

Telephone Code
Let's play an April Fool's joke on Bonnie.

Mystery Riddle
Ronald was in a baseball game. He was running from third base to home and was met by the catcher, who was wearing a catcher's mask. He stopped, ran back to third, and slid in to avoid being tagged.

DETECTIVE CASEFILE 6
THE CASE OF THE
UNFORTUNATE FAN

The man showed Dumpty a whole concert ticket, not the stub. If he had entered the auditorium, the ticket-collector would have torn the ticket in half. Therefore, Dumpty knew the man was lying.

Secret Line Messages
Surprise

Handwriting Analysis
A. 3 (The date is written with the day, month, and year, in that order.)
B. 5 (While the message was being traced, the top paper was shifted, and part of the second and third lines are at an angle.)
C. 2 (Look for the capital letters in the sentences. The message says "IN THE TREE.")

D. 6 (The capital F beginning the first sentence is different from the one beginning the second sentence, showing that the writer tried to disguise his handwriting but forgot to change an F.)

E. 4 (Note the left-handed slant of the letters.)

F. 1 (See how a letter is scratched out and a punctuation mark is missing.)

Mystery Riddle

Frank Cummings happened to be walking home after a hard day's work.

DETECTIVE CASEFILE 7
THE CASE OF THE
BUMBLING BURGLAR

Through the window, Dumpty saw the receiver resting on the telephone cradle.

But he had heard the receiver fall to the floor as Winters supposedly ran after the thief. Caught by his mistake. Winters admitted setting up the robbery.

Questioning the Suspect

1. *Where is your train ticket?* If the passenger were a fleeing criminal, he would have a one-way ticket.

2. *May I see your hands?*
If the man's hands are not heavily calloused, chances are he's not a farmer.

3. *Did the dog bark?*
If not, the robber must have been someone the dog knew — possibly the servant.

Mystery Riddle

The woman fell backwards and landed inside the room.

DETECTIVE CASEFILE 8
THE CASE OF THE DOWN-AND-OUT DELIVERY MAN

Dennis claimed that he was knocked down with only one punch. But if this were true, both his cheeks would not have been bruised unless a very large fist hit him right in the middle of his face. But since the picture shows that Dennis's nose was unharmed, he had to be lying. Dennis soon admitted that he had lied about the robbery and stolen the money himself.

Shopping List Code
See you tonight.

Mystery Riddle
The two girls had another sister. They were triplets.

DETECTIVE CASEFILE 9
THE CASE OF THE
DINER DISASTERS

The picture shows that there were at least three restaurants on Maple Street. Officer Dumpty never told the twins which restaurant's food had been ruined. The only way Tim and Kim could have known it was Pulski's was if they had been there that morning. Once Officer Dumpty pointed this out, Tim and Kim admitted their guilt.

Pigpen Code
Key is in postbox.

Mystery Riddle
The tyre that was flat was the spare one in the squad car's boot.

DETECTIVE CASEFILE 10
THE CASE OF THE
STOLEN EXAM

With his mask on, it was impossible for Tony to drink from the glass he was holding because it had no straw. The mouth of the mask was too small. Tony needed a glass with a straw — the one he had left on the filing cabinet.

Police Lineup

Suspect No 2 is the guilty person. The gash on O'Neill's right cheek shows the robber used his left hand to punch him. The gash was made by a jewelled ring. Suspect No 2 is the only person wearing a ring on his left hand.

Mystery Riddle

It took officer Wallace the same amount of time each way. One hour and twenty minutes is the same as eighty minutes.

You Be The Jury
by *Marvin Miller*

Did Mr Rogers fake his burglary to claim the insurance money?
Is Stanley Woot's last will and testament a fake?
Did John Goode shoot his business partner by accident – or was it attempted murder?

Ten intriguing courtroom mysteries are played out before you. Examine each case, study the evidence, then make your decision. The final verdict is up to you!

You Be The Jury II
by *Marvin Miller*

Here we have twenty more intriguing courtroom mysteries for you to solve.

Which one of the identical Lee twins vandalised Farmer Foley's chicken coup?
Did Brenda Taylor deliberately set fire to her jewellery shop so she could claim the insurance money?

Examine each case, study the evidence, then make your decision. The final verdict is up to you!

You Be The Jury III
by *Marvin Miller* illustrated by *Harry Venning*

Order in the Court!

The court is now in session and *you* are the jury!
In these ten mysterious cases *you* must examine the evidence, *you* spot the clues, and *you* decide the verdict – Guilty or not guilty.

You Be The Detective
by *Marvin Miller*

Can YOU solve the crime?

Seven baffling crimes have been committed, and YOU are the detective. You have to visit the scene of the crime, question the suspects and piece together the clues.

Who Dunnit?
by *Marvin Miller* illustrated by *Harry Venning*

A brilliant book for all budding detectives, with picture puzzle crimes to solve, a complex collection of codes to crack, hints on how to search for clues – in fact, everything you need to become a supersleuth.

HIPPO HUMOUR

COPING WITH . . .

Coping With School
by *Peter Corey* illustrated by *Martin Brown*

Peter Corey is back at school, looking into locker rooms, delving into school dinners and peering into playgrounds. Don't think you can survive the happiest days of your life without this essential guide.

Coping With Parents
by *Peter Corey* illustrated by *Martin Brown*

A must for all parent owners!

Do you have one or more parents? And do you find them a problem? Don't worry – you're not alone in your troubles. In fact, 99% of people questioned admitted that their parents are an aggravation to them!
This book is *your* chance to hit back! Learn what makes parents tick, how to reorganize different types of parents, and then begin a step-by-step programme to getting even!

Coping With Teachers
by *Peter Corey* illustrated by *Martin Brown*

Is everyone always telling you that school days are the best days of your life? Do you wonder how this can possibly be when there's always some teacher lurking around just waiting to spoil all your fun?
In Coping with Teachers, Peter Corey (4b) turns intrepid investigator in an effort to understand what makes teachers tick. He visits the natural habitats of 26 species of teacher, revealing fascinating facts that will shock and amaze.

Coping With Boys/Coping With Girls
by *Peter Corey* and *Kara May*

An unusual interpretation of the battle of the sexes! Peter Corey is back, and this time he's brought a friend. While Peter does battle with the girls, flip over the book and Kara May answers back about boys. From the dawn of history right through to the present day, these two-books-in-one provide an hilarious and illuminating two-sided and sometimes directly contradicting view of the battle of the sexes.

HORRIBLE HISTORIES
History with the nasty bits left in!

The Awesome Egyptians
by *Terry Deary* and *Peter Hepplewhite*

The Awesome Egyptians gives you some awful information about phabulous Pharaohs and poverty-stricken peasants – who lived an awesome 5,000 years ago!

Want to Know:
* which king had the worst blackheads?
* why some kings had to wear false beards?
* why the peasants were revolting?

In this book you'll find some foul facts about death and decay, revolting recipes for 3,000-year-old sweets, how to make a mean mummy, and some awful Egyptian arithmetic.
History has *never* been so horrible!

The Terrible Tudors
by *Terry Deary* and *Neil Tonge*

The Terrible Tudors gives you all the grizzly details of Tudor life for everyone – from cruel kings and queens, to poor peasants and common criminals.

Want to Know:
* some terrible Tudor swear words?
* about terrible Tudor torture?
* why Henry VIII thought he'd married a horse?

Read this book to find some foul facts, some horrendous beheadings, a mysterious murder, some curious quizzes and gruesome games.

History has *never* been so horrible!

HIPPO PUZZLES

The School Puzzle Book
by *Stella Maidment* illustrated by *Steve Donald*

A riotous book that follows the antics of Cheesy and his mates at Nutsville Primary School. Work out Who's Who in the class photo, find an escape route from the nightmare maze and discover some differences in the dinner plates. Also, enjoy Steve Donald's wacky and hilarious cartoon illustrations.

Decode the Deadliest Joke in the Universe
by *Kjartan Poskitt* illustrated by *Tony Blundell*

Do you dare discover the worst joke in the world? Be warned, this puzzle book contains a deadly weapon. Who knows what will happen once you release the Worst Joke in the World! The answer to each puzzle is the answer to a joke. Work out the special coded message, and the deadly weapon will be yours.

Puzzles to Cuddle
by *Tat Small* illustrated by *Tony Blundell*

Lots of cuddly puzzles about everyone's favourite animals, imaginatively created with humorous and appealing illustrations.

Puzzles to Guzzle
by *Tat Small* illustrated by *David Woodward*

Chomp your way through lashings of foody puzzle fun!

The Horribly Hard Hoilday Puzzle Book
by *Steve Weatherill*

A holiday puzzle book with a difference! No traveller should be without this riotous book of holiday puzzles! With hilarious illustrations and some wildly unusual puzzles, no matter how you're travelling, time will fly by!

The Monster Fun Book
by *Steve Smallman*

All sorts of creepy creatures inhabit this gruesome book. It's bursting with monstrous puzzles, freaky facts and gigantic jokes. There's even space to design your own four-eyed swamp monster to cut-out and make up.